Happy

Lots of love

Carol xxx

MOTHER ALWAYS SAID...

Viv Quillin

'Sorry
I spoke!'

VICTOR GOLLANCZ

First published in Great Britain 1995
by Victor Gollancz
A Division of the Cassell group
Villiers House, 41/47 Strand, London WC2N 5JE

A catalogue record for this book is available from the British Library

ISBN 0 575 05925 7

Designed by Robert Updegraff
Printed in Hong Kong by Imago Publishing Limited

*Dedicated to all mums
and special thanks to Ali*

'You eat like a bird'

'You don't know you're born'

'Just like his father'

'You don't want that'

'What's the matter *now*?'

'You'll grow into it'

'You should have gone before we came out'

'It doesn't hurt that much'

'Bit short isn't it?'

'He seems a nice boy'

'Enjoy yourself while you're young'

'This hurts me more than it hurts you'

'We haven't all had your advantages'

'Of course I understand, I'm your mother'

'But I only said . . .'

'Wow! Have you heard the new
Pink Floyd Album?'

'Funny how people think I'm your sister'

'Simmer down, dear'

'The Smythes' daughter is *such* a pleasant girl'

'Say if you don't like it'

'I'll *never* forget you wetting the bed that time'

'Where did I go wrong?'

'Anyone would think you don't like living at home'

'Too sensitive, that's your trouble'

'Oh yes, you'd do anything for your father'

'You treat this place like a hotel'

'Ask *nicely*'

'Just pretend I'm not here'

'Got herself pregnant'

'When are you going to settle down?'

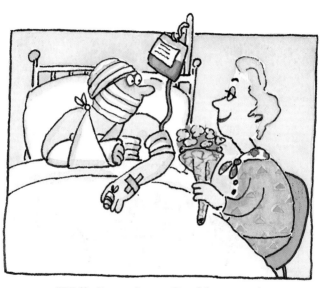

'Well, I won't say I told you so'

'*Lovely* to hear your voice, darling . . .
it's been such a long time'

'Don't worry about me, dear'

'Still no sign of Mister Right?'

'You're all I've got'

'You'll be bored with it in ten minutes'

'This will kill your father'

'Nobody's going to be looking at you'

'Very nice, dear'

'We're not at home to Mister Crosspatch'

'I could have been a famous ballerina,
but I met your dad'

'Nobody wants you when you're old'

'I'm your mother, so I'm allowed to'

'Nothing beats my chicken soup'

'You'll thank me one day'

'I won't say a *word*'